Use these stickers for the activities in the book

Page 2

Page 6

Here's a jug!
Here's a jewel!

Page 7

Page 14

Page 17

th th th th

Page 18

ee ee ea ea

Page 20

Ow! Wow!

ou ou ou

Page 21

Here's a crown!
Here's a flower!

Page 5

ai
ay ay ai

Page 8

n n
kn kn

Page 11

m m
m m

Page 12

oo ew
ou ue

Page 15

b b b b

Page 22

t t t t

Page 24

cry moon
just then
fire black
turn part
milk

Well done!
Well done!
Well done!
Well done!
Well done!
Well done!
Well done!
Well done!
Well done!
Well done!
Well done!

Reading Together

The Princess
and the Pea

Phonics Consultant: Susan Purcell
Illustrator: Charlotte Cooke
Concept: Fran Bromage

Miles
Kelly

As you read aloud, focus on the **cr** and **pr** blends

Once upon a time, there was a **pr**oud **pr**ince, who lived a happy life in a **cr**eepy old castle, but he was a bit lonely.

Say the words as you spot each thing.

Stick on their stickers.

prince

crown

creepers

One day, the prince's father, the king, cried, "Let's cross our country and find you a princess."

What a good try! Put a gold star here.

Sound out these words, which all use the **cr** and **pr** blends.

crab   crow   crunch   cry
price   press   pretty

3

The family stayed in some great palaces.

Princesses came from near and far, aiming to impress the waiting prince.

Say the names of the things in the picture as you spot them. They all use the ai sound.

waiter   plate   face   cake

4

Mostly, the princesses behaved well, but some were vain, some were lazy and some just wanted the cake!

Use your stickers to **spell** some words that use the **ai** sound.

st**ay** pl**ay** sn**ai**l tr**ai**n

The prince did meet a lovely princess called Julia, who seemed just right.

But sadly Julia had terrible manners and ate gigantic mouthfuls of food! She just wouldn't do either!

Use your arrow stickers to **point** to two things beginning with j

Sound out these words with the j sound.

job   jelly   jumper   join

giraffe   giant   gentle

The prince returned to his faraway castle feeling sad.

One night there was a fearsome storm. Fierce lightning lit up the sky. It was so cold that everyone stayed close by the fire.

Say the words as you spot things with the f sound.

Stick on their stickers.

fire

fur

feet

7

In the middle of the **n**ight, there was a loud **kn**ocking at the door.

It was such a **n**asty **n**ight, the queen felt **n**ervous about the **n**oise.

Use your stickers to **spell** some words beginning with the n sound.

neck   noon   knit   knee

When they heard the knocking again they opened the door.

There stood a girl with dripping wet, curly hair.

Point out the ur sound (as in curly)

Sound out these words, which all use the ur sound.

learn   search   stir   bird

turn   nurse   purple

The king invited the girl in. He gave her a chair by the fire, so she could dry her hair.

The prince couldn't help but stare at her.

Sound out these words with the air sound.

fair   pair   share   square

bear   wear   there

10

The girl sipped a mug of warm milk, and tried not to make a mess on the carpet.

Use your stickers to **spell** some words, which all use the **m** sound.

mat   met   mud   mix

Soon, the girl grew warm and dry. Now she was in a much better mood.

"Who ARE you?" asked the prince. The girl told him she was a princess!

Use your stickers to **spell** some words with the **oo** sound.

spoon   chew   group   blue

12

The queen didn't believe this.

"Let's prepare a room and prove whether she is a true princess," thought the queen.

Sound out some more words with the **oo** sound.

moon   roof   clue   glue

soup   move   fruit

Emphasize the b sound (as in bed)

As the maids began to make the girl's bed, the queen balanced a pea on the bottom of the bedstead.

Say the words as you spot things with the b sound.

Stick on their stickers.

14

bed

banner

bow

"She will have a beastly night's sleep if she is a real princess," said the queen, "because she will feel a big lump in the bed!"

Use your stickers to **spell** some words with the **b** sound.

back **b**ird **b**oat **b**end

Then, onto that bed the maids piled twenty mattresses with twenty feather quilts on top of one another.

When the quilts were smooth the maids left.

Sound out the words thin and they. Can you hear the difference?

Sound out some words with the hard th sound.

these   those   other

weather   brother   rather

16

The prince's mother fetched the girl from the other room and there she was left for the night.

Use your stickers to **spell** some words with the hard **th** sound.

this   there   father   together

In the morning, the queen swept into the girl's room. "Tell me, how did you sleep?" she asked.

The girl could barely speak. "I'm so tired, I could weep," she squeaked.

Use your stickers to **spell** some words with the **ee** sound.

sheet   tree   dream   meat

18

"I didn't sleep at all," the girl blurted out. "There was a lump under the blankets. I'm black and blue all over!"

Sound out some words with the bl blend.

blast   blend   block   blink
blow   blunt   bless

19

There was no doubt about the girl now. Only a princess would have felt a little round pea in the bed.

When the prince found out, he gave a shout of joy.

Stick on the speech bubbles for the prince and princess.

Use your stickers to **complete** the sentence with the **ow** sound.

When the prince found out, he gave a shout of joy.

The prince vowed to marry the princess, and astounded her by asking her right away. They didn't hang about!

Use your arrow stickers to **point** to two things with the ow sound.

Sound out some more words with the ow sound.

cow   brown   town

ground   mouth   amount

21

And what do you think happened to that special little pea?

It was placed in the royal museum – where it probably still is today.

Use your stickers to **spell** some words with the t sound.

team   table   boot   part

Ask your child to **retell** the story using
these key sounds and story images.

prince

waiting

night

girl

stare

true

bed

sleep

vowed

23

Use your stickers to **add** a word that matches
the red highlighted **sounds** on each line.

creepy   crow   crab   ☐

giant   jelly   gentle

fur   feeling   fierce

heard   curly   bird

mug   mix   mess

blue   roof   true

they   rather   with

blow   blanket   blink

today   team   that

24

You've had fun with phonics! Well done.